GROW YOUR OWN
FIREWOOD

How to create a productive woodland

MICHAEL LITTLEWOOD

ECODESIGNSCAPE
Somerset England

Beechwood fires are bright and clear,
If the logs are kept a year;
Chestnut only good they say,
If for long it's laid away;
Make a fire of elder tree,
Death within your house shall be.
But ash new or ash old,
Is fit for Queen with crown of gold.

Birch and fir logs burn too fast,
Blaze up bright and do not last;
It is by the Irish said
Hawthorn bakes the sweetest bread;
Elmwood burns like churchyard mould –
E'en the flames are very cold.
But ash green or ash brown,
Is fit for Queen with golden crown.

Poplar gives a bitter smoke,
Fills your eyes and makes you choke;
Apple wood will scent your room,
With incense-like perfume.
Oaken logs, if dry and old,
Will keep away the winter's cold;
But ash wet or ash dry
A king shall warm his slippers by.

Anon.

GROW YOUR OWN FIREWOOD

Published by

Ecodesignscape
Hinton St. George,
Somerset TA17 8SD

ISBN: 978-0-9563628-6-5

Edited by Gaby Bartai

Designed by Andrew Crane

Drawings by Ian Osman

Printed by Orbit Digital, Wiltshire

CONTENTS

INTRODUCTION

THROUGHOUT HISTORY country people have worked in woodlands: woodsmen felled timber for construction and 'cord' for firewood, swineherds brought pigs to feed on beechmast and acorns, and charcoal burners provided fuel for the iron-smelting furnaces. A single woodland, systematically cut and felled in rotation, would generate sustainable supplies of durable hardwoods such as oak, sweet chestnut, ash and beech for a multitude of uses ranging from fuel to furniture. Woodland was a hugely valued resource.

Once, Britain was covered by continuous dense forest; today, barely 10% of the UK is woodland. As the glaciers retreated and the climate warmed after the last Ice Age, pioneer tree species recolonised the land. The first trees were pines, junipers and birches. In the more favourable areas of the country, these in time gave way to broadleaved trees such as elm, oak, ash and lime.

Gradually, man began to clear areas of woodland, first for hunting, then for grazing animals, and then for arable agriculture. By Roman times, a patchwork landscape of woodland, agricultural and developed areas was emerging. Much of the remaining woodland survived up until the Industrial Revolution, however, because it was a vital source of essential products for building and fuel. This had all changed by the turn of the 20th century, because industrial agriculture offered a more profitable way to use the land and cheap alternative fuels and building materials were becoming available.

Planting woodland for firewood can be seen as a return to more traditional and sustainable forms of land use. A well-managed woodland is a sustainable resource, and any landowner could well benefit from establishing a small wood on their property, especially as a source of wood for fuel. With the ever-increasing cost of energy, and potential problems with future oil and gas supplies, especially from the Middle East, it makes economic sense to devote at least one hectare – or even just one acre – of a property to woodland.

As more people realise the value of wood fuel and invest in wood-burning stoves, demand for logs is outstripping supply, with the result that firewood has to be harvested from a whole range of locations, including roadsides, commercial and industrial estates and wasteland. By creating your own woodland, you will be helping to supply this shortfall.

This guide is concerned primarily with the establishment of trees over the first 10 to 15 years, mainly for the purpose of providing firewood. There will be the opportunity for producing some timber for other uses, ranging from building projects to beanpoles. A woodland also offers the opportunity for landscape improvement, creates habitats for wildlife, shelters crops, livestock and buildings, and has many other potential uses, depending on the area of land available. Owners of small woods often prefer multipurpose management, which helps to ensure that their woodland is self-sustaining and economically viable.

A woodland is a wonderful asset, offering far more than the practical benefits of firewood and timber, valuable as these are. Having your own productive woodland and becoming self-sufficient in firewood can be a source of great pride and pleasure; laying down stores of wood for winters to come gives you a huge sense of satisfaction as well as the guarantee of a warm house! A woodland is also a wonderful landscape amenity and a place of sanctuary, beauty and peace. It can be a space for recreation, relaxation, reflection or the enjoyment of nature, at all times of the year.

This book is divided into three main sections. The first covers the planning and design of a new woodland, and the best choice of species. The second covers the requirements for putting the plan into action: selecting the correct stock, ground preparation, and the planting of the trees and shrubs. The final section is concerned with protecting, maintaining and harvesting the trees, ensuring the success of the project in years to come. It also considers the best ways to bring existing woodland into productive management.

Trees, alongside water and landform, are the main components of the British landscape, and a key element of its beauty and character.

Preparation

1 | PLANNING

To create a successful productive woodland, you need to start with a plan.

CAREFUL PLANNING IS KEY to achieving a productive woodland, whatever its size. It is essential that you have an overall Woodland Plan, prepared either by yourself or – ideally – by a professional. While planning, designing, planting and maintaining a woodland is a hugely rewarding project, it can be daunting for those without previous experience, and the expertise of a professional can be invaluable.

Prospective owners of woodland often assume that a plan will be costly, time-consuming or difficult to produce, or that a plan is only appropriate for a large-scale commercial operation. In fact, the process of creating a plan is straightforward, having one will save you time and money, and it is an essential tool for managing a woodland, whatever its size.

A productive woodland can – and should – provide habitats for all types of wildlife, and care must be taken to ensure that management operations cause it no harm.

Photo: Martin Palmer – www.bedsflorafauna.blogspot.com

A Woodland Plan is a detailed document that assesses your site as it is today and sets out how best to reach your objectives for the creation of a productive woodland on your property. The process of creating the plan will help you clarify your aims and objectives for your woodland, and allow you to assess the opportunities and constraints of possible sites. It will help you identify appropriate areas for the different elements in your woodland design, let you create a woodland that is attractive as well as functional, and ensure that it is designed in harmony with nature.

When your plan is complete, you will have a clear vision of how to proceed. It will ensure that your planting plans are based on sound decisions, and help you avoid the risk of costly and time-consuming mistakes. Without a plan, it is far too easy to find yourself wishing that you had thought things through before starting work. Your plan will set out a logical and budgeted programme of work, which will let you work methodically towards your goals and ensure that you achieve your objectives.

A Woodland Plan will also assist with grant aid applications. As of 2014 all grants from the Forestry Commission in England are likely to need a management plan attached. Eventually, even felling licences may need to be attached to a plan. Your plan will equip you with a clear, mapped record of your planting proposals and management objectives to include with any applications you may make.

A plan is also invaluable when, in the fullness of time, you hand on your woodland to new management. Given the longevity of trees, a common problem in small woodlands is that different owners pursue different objectives, because previous owners have left no record of what they were trying to achieve. A plan can help to ensure that your long-term objectives for your woodland will be realised – even if you are not there to see it happen.

The form your plan takes is up to you; you can make handwritten notes and drawings, or create digital maps and plans. Programmes for planning and mapping woodland are available online.

The planning process

Planning involves several key steps:

1. Aims, objectives & resources

The first step is to identify your objectives in planting trees and woodland. Your main aim is probably the production of firewood, but you also need to identify any other requirements you have, such as the production of timber for building and fencing, landscape improvement, the establishment of shelter, and the creation of wildlife habitats. You also need to assess how much time, energy and money you are able to invest in the project.

2. Survey

The next step is to undertake a survey of your land to identify potential opportunities for new woodland and assess the possible constraints on proposed planting areas. Make detailed notes about all the physical, natural and visual features of the possible sites. Survey existing copses, spinneys and linear woodlands, and assess their suitability for expansion. Observe which tree and shrub species are already growing well on your land, and in your area. Use your local library, or online sources, to research data about the historical, physical, natural and visual features of the site, and obtain maps and aerial photographs. You can apply for a paper map of your woodland from the Forestry Commission by downloading the Map Request Form from their website. Alternatively, you can search for your woodland on Google Earth, and then view and print it as a map or an aerial photograph.

3. Analysis

Having completed your survey, you should then produce an analysis of your findings. This involves assessing the opportunities and constraints you have identified, considering

An aerial view of the site is very useful when planning the design of a woodland.

Site survey plan

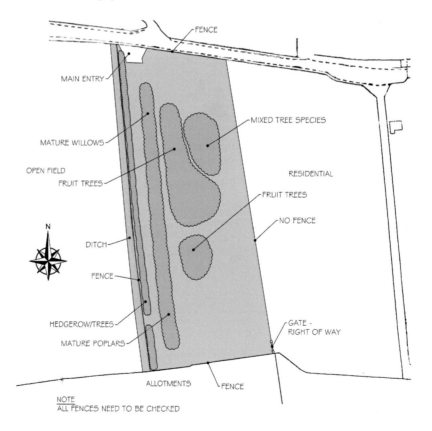

natural factors such as soil, topography and exposure and also visual ones such as landscape character. Doing this lets you work out what is actually possible. You may discover that some of your objectives are not achievable, but it is far better to realise that now, and find workable alternatives.

4. Design

You then need to decide on the best type of woodland for your site, plan the layout of the woodland, and select the species you will plant. Having done so, draw a map of your proposals at the appropriate scale. Your map should have accompanying notes describing the type of woodland and listing the tree species.

5. Management methods

The next step is to make decisions about the best management techniques for your new woodland, on the basis of all the information in your survey and analysis. Key decisions are what type of stock to plant, the method of ground preparation, what planting technique to use, how to protect the trees, the maintenance techniques to be used, and how to harvest the wood. Where you are incorporating existing woodland into your design, you also need to make decisions about how to bring this into productive management.

6. Work programme

Finally, you need to work out what action is required to achieve each of your objectives. Having done so, you can organise the tasks involved into a logical sequence, phased according to your available time, energy and budget. A detailed programme of work covering labour, materials, timescales and costs can then be produced.

Site analysis plan

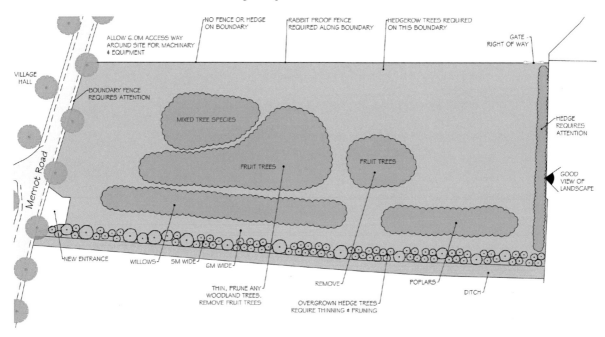

VILLAGE HALL

Merriot Road

ALLOW 6.0M ACCESS WAY AROUND SITE FOR MACHINARY & EQUIPMENT

BOUNDARY FENCE REQUIRES ATTENTION

NO FENCE OR HEDGE ON BOUNDARY

RABBIT PROOF FENCE REQUIRED ALONG BOUNDARY

HEDGEROW TREES REQUIRED ON THIS BOUNDARY

GATE - RIGHT OF WAY

MIXED TREE SPECIES

FRUIT TREES

FRUIT TREES

HEDGE REQUIRES ATTENTION

GOOD VIEW OF LANDSCAPE

NEW ENTRANCE

WILLOWS

5M WIDE

6M WIDE

THIN, PRUNE ANY WOODLAND TREES. REMOVE FRUIT TREES

OVERGROWN HEDGE TREES REQUIRE THINNING & PRUNING

REMOVE

POPLARS

DITCH

Design proposal

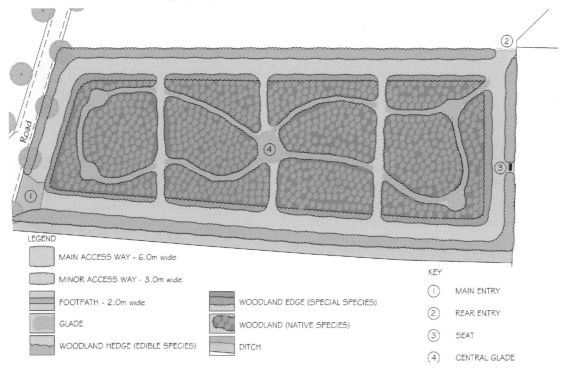

Road

②

④

③

①

LEGEND

MAIN ACCESS WAY - 6.0m wide	
MINOR ACCESS WAY - 3.0m wide	
FOOTPATH - 2.0m wide	WOODLAND EDGE (SPECIAL SPECIES)
GLADE	WOODLAND (NATIVE SPECIES)
WOODLAND HEDGE (EDIBLE SPECIES)	DITCH

KEY

① MAIN ENTRY

② REAR ENTRY

③ SEAT

④ CENTRAL GLADE

Benefits of a Woodland Plan

Your plan will:

- Identify the appropriate areas for the various elements of your woodland
- Show how all the features of the site can be utilised in harmony with nature
- Improve productivity whilst protecting and benefiting the environment
- Ensure the conservation and enhancement of the site's natural resources
- Set out a logical programme of work
- Allow work to be phased according to budget
- Identify future requirements and further possibilities for the site
- Provide a permanent record for the whole project
- Act as a focus for continued motivation
- Support any grant aid applications
- Allow you to enjoy the experience of managing a woodland

Record-keeping

The planning phase does not end when the actual work starts; it is also important to keep careful records of the work you do. Woodland management is a long-term project, and you should not rely on your memory! Only by writing things down will you be able to remember accurately what work was carried out, where, when, how and why. You will need this information in order to make the right management decisions in future years. It will also allow you to provide evidence of compliance with the legal obligations of woodland management, such as obtaining felling licences and managing protected habitats.

2 DESIGN

A thorough assessment of your site conditions will ensure that you make the right design decisions for your new woodland.

Key design considerations

- Location
- Size and yield
- Soil and aspect
- Category and type of woodland
- Plant layers
- Layout
- Choice of species
- Tree spacing

Location

Most land is suitable for growing trees for firewood. Woodland trees are generally much less demanding in terms of soil and climate than other crops, so woods have traditionally been sited on land that is left once higher-grade soils have been allocated to arable crops and grazing. This includes steep slopes, poorly drained soils, infertile sandy soils, and very exposed locations in upland areas. You can also use field corners that are difficult to work, areas of rough ground, or fields too small or awkward for grazing or arable crops. The ideal site, however, is flat and well-drained with easy access for machinery and vehicles.

Care must be taken on steep slopes, which may need to be terraced. Planting trees on slopes is a very effective way of protecting the soil from erosion, provided that continuous

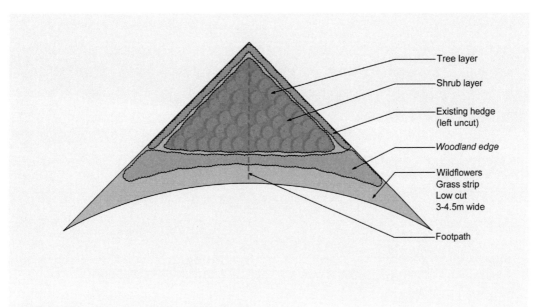

Tree layer

Shrub layer

Existing hedge
(left uncut)

Woodland edge

Wildflowers
Grass strip
Low cut
3-4.5m wide

Footpath

Field corner planting – one field

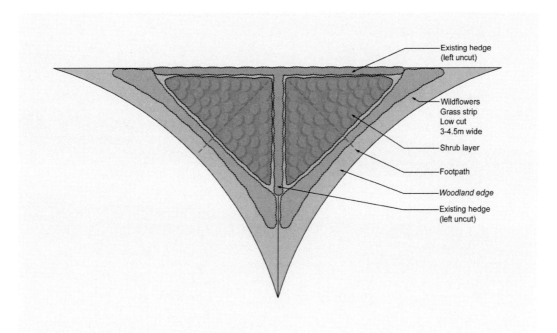

Existing hedge
(left uncut)

Wildflowers
Grass strip
Low cut
3-4.5m wide

Shrub layer

Footpath

Woodland edge

Existing hedge
(left uncut)

Field corner planting – two fields

Here, trees have been planted on a steep slope with no control of surface water run-off. This could result in erosion and insufficient water for the young trees and even exposure of their roots, resulting in death. The creation of narrow terraces and the addition of ground cover plants would overcome this problem.

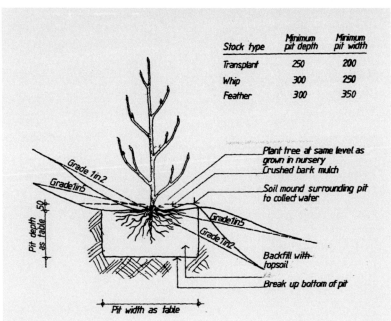

Stock type	Minimum pit depth	Minimum pit width
Transplant	250	200
Whip	300	250
Feather	300	350

Plant tree at same level as grown in nursery
Crushed bark mulch

Soil mound surrounding pit to collect water

Backfill with topsoil

Break up bottom of pit

Grade 1in 2
Grade 1in 5
Grade 1in 5
Grade 1in 2

Pit depth as table 50

Pit width as table

Planting on slopes

cover forestry or coppicing is practised. Clear-felling would leave the soil even more vulnerable.

Planting trees in blocks can make harvesting easier, as long as good access is incorporated. An alternative is to create woodland belts or strips across your site. This enables woodland to be incorporated into a farm or smallholding without sacrificing any productive land. Existing copses and spinneys can often be used as a basis for new woodland extensions, with hedgerows, especially those alongside roads and lanes, being converted into linear woodland. This is a useful approach where space for new woodland is limited.

Trees are not appropriate everywhere, however. You need to consider the impact of your proposed woodland on the landscape, not only as it is growing but when it is coppiced or felled. Avoid planting trees where they will block scenic views, or on wetland or grassland which is species-rich or important for nesting birds. Check that your intended planting site does

The hedgerows on either side of this disused drover's track could be allowed to become a linear woodland by discontinuing cutting or flailing.

not have conservation status that rules out the planting of trees, or requires you to obtain special permission to do so. Do not plant trees close to underground pipes or cables or overhead power lines. You should also avoid planting up field corners next to road junctions, as this may impede visibility for motorists in the future.

Size

It is useful to think in terms of three categories of woodland for the purposes of management:

Small woods

These are under 2 hectares (5 acres). Even areas of less than one hectare can be used to supply some firewood and timber for occasional building projects, and they are also valuable in terms of landscape improvement and wildlife conservation – small woods often have greater importance in the landscape than their size suggests.

Medium woods

The area of this category is from 2 to 6ha (5 to 15 acres). These woods should be divided into compartments of 0.5 to 1ha for working. On this scale it is possible to produce a sustained yield of firewood, as well as small-size timber for building projects, fence posts and rails.

Large woods

These woods are 6ha (15 acres) and upwards, and can produce sufficient firewood to sell in addition to supplying your own needs. They can also be developed for a range of additional uses, including the production of timber for building.

Note: 1 hectare is equal to 2.471 acres. 1 hectare has dimensions of 100m by 100m.

Yield

Quantity of firewood required

The quantity of wood needed to heat a house depends on the size and design of the property, the type of heating system and its efficiency, how well insulated the house is, and the temperature required by the occupants. Any of these factors can make a major difference to the amount of wood required.

A typical three-bedroom house, which is draught-proofed and insulated and has a woodburner of a suitable size, will require approximately three tonnes of air-dried wood for heating over the course of a year. This figure may well reduce as insulation and heating systems become more efficient.

Estimated yield

Although mature trees can be felled and cut up for use as firewood, more manageable log sizes can be produced on a more sustainable basis by coppicing, and this is generally the best way of managing a small woodland for firewood. Coppicing – the practice of cutting trees down to ground level on a rotational basis – takes advantage of the fact that many broadleaved species readily resprout from cut stumps. This allows wood to be harvested on a regular cycle. (See Chapter 9 for detailed information on coppicing.)

A well-managed coppiced woodland containing a full stocking of mixed broadleaved species should produce six tonnes of green timber per hectare annually. Once it has been dried, this will give you three tonnes of air-dried wood. One hectare of coppiced woodland on good quality land should therefore produce enough firewood to heat a typical three-bedroom house. If you have a smaller area of land available, wood can of course be used to supplement other sources of heat.

However, this should only be taken as a broad guide to your likely harvest. Estimates of yield per hectare, and indeed of how much wood is needed to heat a house, vary enormously. The figures quoted here are the general consensus, but some sources quote as much as three hectares, or as little as a seventh of a hectare, to produce an annual harvest of three tonnes of air-dried wood. The Forestry Commission is currently undertaking more research on the subject.

Actual yield depends on the location of the woodland and environmental factors such as climate, soil and topography, and can vary hugely. A mixed-species woodland on good lowland soil can produce five times the yield of woodland on poor mountainside soil. It is therefore impossible to give a definitive forecast of yield, and the best advice is to plant as much woodland as you have the space to accommodate and the time to care for. Any surplus firewood will always find a market.

Soil & aspect

It is essential to match the type of woodland and the species you plant to the soil conditions and aspect of your site. Many trees will tolerate challenging conditions, but you will get much better results if you plant the trees most suited to the conditions you have.

See Table 1: *Suitability of Firewood Tree Species to Site Conditions*

Soil

Where soil, topography and climatic conditions are good, most tree species will grow, but trees, like any plant, have particular soil, climatic and other preferences, with an optimum combination where they will do best. Some native tree species will grow reasonably well on almost any soil, over a wide range of climatic conditions, but others are more specific in their requirements.

Soil pH and soil type are crucial factors which are often overlooked. Soil pH should normally fall between 5 and 7.5,

Table 1
Suitability of Firewood Tree Species to Site Conditions

Botanical Name	Common Name	High Altitude	Frost Pockets	Exposure To Wind	Near Sea	Shade	Contaminated Ground
Acer campestre	Field maple			•			
Acer pseudoplatanus	Sycamore			•			•
Alnus glutinosa	Common alder	•					•
Betula pendula	Birch		•	•			•
Buxus sempervirens	Box		•	•		•	
Carpinus betulus	Hornbeam		•				
Castanea sativa	Sweet chestnut				•		
Corylus avellana	Hazel	•					
Crataegus monogyna	Hawthorn			•	•		
Fagus sylvatica	Beech			•		•	
Fraxinus excelsior	Ash	•	•	•		•	
Ilex aquifolium	Holly	•			•		
Juniperus communis	Juniper	•		•	•		
Malus sylvestris	Crab apple				•		
Pinus sylvestris	Scots pine	•	•	•			
Populus tremula	Aspen	•		•	•		
Prunus avium	Wild cherry	•		•			•
Prunus padus	Bird cherry	•	•			•	
Quercus robur	Oak		•				
Sorbus aria	Whitebeam			•	•		•
Sorbus aucuparia	Rowan	•		•	•		•

Table 2
Suitability of Firewood Tree Species to Soil Types

Botanical Name	Common Name	Wet / Moist	Heavy	Neutral / Alkaline	Acid	Light / Dry
Acer campestre	Field maple		•	•		•
Acer pseudoplatanus	Sycamore	•				
Alnus glutinosa	Common alder	•		•	•	
Betula pendula	Birch	•	•	•	•	•
Buxus sempervirens	Box			•		
Carpinus betulus	Hornbeam	•		•		
Castanea sativa	Sweet chestnut				•	•
Corylus avellana	Hazel	•				•
Crataegus monogyna	Hawthorn	•	•	•	•	•
Fagus sylvatica	Beech			•		•
Fraxinus excelsior	Ash	•	•	•		•
Ilex aquifolium	Holly			•		•
Juniperus communis	Juniper			•		•
Malus sylvestris	Crab apple		•	•		•
Pinus sylvestris	Scots pine					•
Populus tremula	Aspen		•	•		•
Prunus avium	Wild cherry		•	•		
Prunus padus	Bird cherry	•		•	•	
Quercus robur	Oak	•	•	•	•	
Sorbus aria	Whitebeam	•		•	•	•
Sorbus aucuparia	Rowan			•	•	•

Preferences of tree species

- Aspen and birch can be found on a wide range of soils. Aspen prefers waterlogged soil, however.
- Beech prefers lime-rich soils and dislikes waterlogged soils.
- Alder and bird cherry prefer moist, streamside locations on mildly acidic soils.
- Wild cherry grows best on fertile soils.
- Juniper and field maple prefer rich but drier soils.
- Sycamore and lime dislike dry conditions.
- Hornbeam and common oak grow best on deep moist clay soils.
- Hazel and hawthorn do well on limestone.
- Sweet chestnut needs acidic, sandy soil to be vigorous.
- Oak can grow well on relatively infertile soil, but is rarely found on thin chalk or limestone soils.
- Elm is generally found on more fertile soils.
- Maple tends to be found on soils with a high clay content.
- Ash is relatively tolerant of waterlogging.
- Pine and downy birch prefer acidic soil.
- Scots pine cannot tolerate a wet soil.

although some species are suitable for more acidic or alkaline soils. It is essential to obtain data relating to soil type for an intended woodland or existing wood. Soil and geological data can be obtained from Cranfield University (see Resources).

A tree's main requirement is for a growing medium that is well-drained and aerated, but which retains sufficient moisture to ensure survival and adequate growth. If your soil is prone to

Water in a woodland is a valuable asset, especially for wildlife, as it increases biodiversity. With a high water table the creation of a pond is a relatively easy task to undertake. This will also enhance the visual and aesthetic appeal of the wood.

waterlogging, do not plant species which are intolerant of wet conditions. Very wet and very dry soils should be avoided if possible.

See Table 2: *Suitability of Firewood Tree Species to Soil Types*

Aspect

Solar orientation and the availability of sunlight are important factors. You should consider whether adjoining hillsides, woodlands and other landscape features will have an impact on your potential site.

However, trees need moisture more than they need warmth, so north- and east-facing slopes, which dry out less in summer, can be better for their growth than south- and west-facing ones. On gently sloping or flat land, it can be beneficial to plant up the north and east sides of the site with robust species that will cope with exposure and also offer shelter and protection to the other trees.

Categories of woodland

Throughout the United Kingdom there are different categories and types of woodland influenced by all the local natural environmental factors, notably climate, geology, soil, topography and hydrology. These locally distinctive woodlands contribute to a visually inspiring landscape and its local character. Sadly, many recent plantings have not recognised these conditions and are not appropriate to their locality.

Given thoughtful design and planting, your new woodland will, in time, make an important contribution to the overall local character of the landscape, at the same time as being productive.

Broadleaved

These typically consist of dominant species such as oak, ash, wild cherry and sweet chestnut. If managed correctly, such woodlands will produce high-value crops in the long term (60 years). Thinnings can be taken throughout the life of the woodland, starting when it is 20 to 25 years old in the case of

Broadleaved woodland generally has more wildlife value and aesthetic appeal, and if it is managed on a coppice cycle it can produce a good yield of firewood in a relatively short time.

types of vegetation. In the south of England they grow on sandy soils. Sometimes birch and larch colonise the gaps in these woods. Pines are fast-growing and are able to provide an early harvest of timber.

However, while names such as oakwood and beechwood indicate the prevalence of one type of tree, most woodlands are naturally a mixture of species. The predominance of particular species in native woodlands in part reflects the fact that man has selected those trees of most use to him, at the expense of other species. Oak and beech, in particular, have been favoured over species such as ash, elm and lime, with the result that British woodlands have become dominated by these more commercially valuable species.

Plant layers

What distinguishes woodland from habitats such as grassland or heathland is its much greater vertical dimension. This provides a series of interconnected habitats, ranging from ground level up to 20 or 30m. It is usual to consider the plants of a woodland in several distinct layers. However, they interact in a complex way, with many wildlife species and some plants moving freely between the different layers.

Tree layer

Also known as the canopy, this comprises the dominant and other equally tall trees, such as oak, ash and beech.

Second tree layer

This consists of trees whose crowns come below those of the trees in the first layer. They are very often younger trees that have not reached the upper canopy level.

Shrub layer

Also known as the understorey, this consists of shrubby plants such as hazel, hawthorn, bramble and holly. This group may overlap with the second tree layer, because some shrubs, such as hazel and hawthorn, can grow to a size comparable with trees.

Diagram showing plant layers

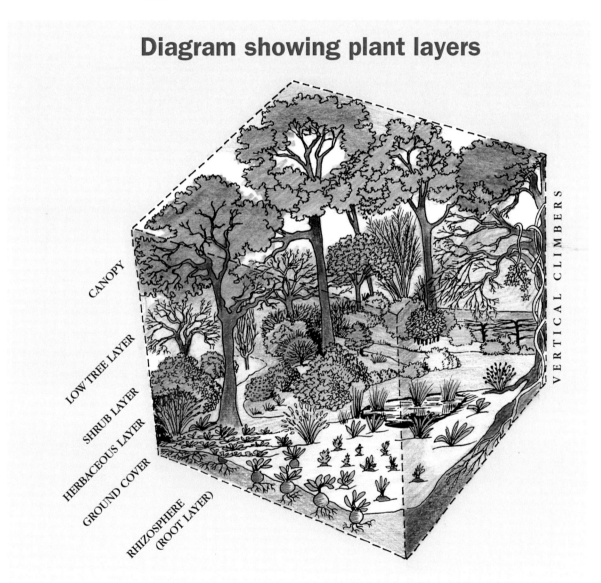

Field layer

Also known as the herb layer, this consists of woody plants less than 1m tall which can tolerate shade, principally wild flowers and ferns.

Ground layer

This consists of the small plants, mainly mosses, which grow on the floor of the wood.

Some woodlands have all five layers well developed. However, it is more usual to find woodlands which lack one or more layers. The most likely reason for this is that the tree layer is too dense, meaning that not enough light filters through to allow the other layers to develop properly.

Woodland edge

The edges of a woodland are usually the most valuable areas in terms of visual amenity and wildlife habitats. They occur not only on the perimeter of the woodland but also along its accessways, roads, rides and glades. Large blocks of woodland have very little edge in proportion to their area. Small woods, and especially linear woods, have much more.

Giving your woodland an irregular outline by planting the perimeter with shrubs of local provenance

RIDE   GROUND LAYER   SHRUB LAYER   SMALLER TREE LAYER   MAIN TREE LAYER

The woodland edge is home to a huge diversity of flora and fauna, so needs to be managed with particular sensitivity, especially in the bird nesting season.

will improve its appearance in the landscape as well as adding to its wildlife value. Plant suitable shrub species at irregular or random spacings, leaving some gaps for colonisation by incoming seeds. Species should be selected to create a sloping woodland edge, which will eventually give a natural layered or 'cascade' effect. This will help to deflect wind and create warmth and stability within the wood. It will shelter your young trees whilst they establish and provide more favourable conditions for pollinating insects.

Alternatively, to achieve the same functional benefits, you could plant a perimeter hedgerow around your new woodland.

Rides & glades

Glades should be around one and a half to two and a half times as wide as the height of the surrounding trees. Rides should be at least 3m (10ft) wide for vehicle access. Rides which are curved or zigzagged avoid undesirable wind-tunnelling effects.

Your design for your woodland should incorporate rides (tracks) and glades (open spaces). At a functional level, these provide access into and through the woodland, and areas where vehicles can be turned and harvested logs can be stacked. The width of the rides and the size of the glades needs to reflect the size of the vehicles and machinery you will be using.

The provision of rides and glades also creates access for people wanting to enjoy the woodland. They also admit light to the woodland floor and create more woodland edge, increasing its biodiversity and wildlife value.

Rides are essential in a woodland as they introduce space and light, thereby increasing biodiversity. Many plants will grow along their edges before the trees come into leaf, and when the tree canopies reduce the light, other species grow to cover the ground. Rides also provide access for working and for machinery, and they are interesting visually because of the contrast of coming out of a dark wood and into the light.

Layout

There are three ways of laying out a woodland: trees can be planted in groups, in rows or in an intimate mixture.

Groups

Planting trees in groups, varying from nine to 21 of each species, helps to ensure their survival and results in a blended look, emulating natural processes. However, if whole groups are struck by disease or storm damage, large areas of the woodland can be left empty.

The ground immediately around each tree needs to be kept clear of competing vegetation, but leaving – or sowing – grass between the rows will make the whole area much more attractive.

Photo: The National Forest

Rows

This option is the easiest to manage and suits the use of machinery for planting, maintenance and harvesting. It is generally the best option for larger productive woodlands, and is obviously not an option for very small ones.

You should avoid planting different species in alternate rows, especially on sloping ground, as this can create what is known as the 'pyjama pattern', because of the obvious stripes that are visible from a distance. Alternate-row planting can,

Here, linear woodland has been allowed to develop from the hedgerows along the sides of a road.

however, be a useful way of getting an early yield if one species is harvested ahead of the other – and this also removes the 'stripes'.

Intimate mixture

This is a random mix of different tree species. In appearance it is the most desirable, but it can be difficult to achieve. Failure to manage it correctly will result in the faster-growing species shading out the slower ones. Planting single-species groups or drifts is a better way of ensuring that all species are represented throughout the life of a woodland.

3 TREE SELECTION

It is important to choose the best species for your site conditions – but the range of possibilities is inspiring.

WHERE SOIL AND CLIMATIC CONDITIONS ARE GOOD, many species will grow well. However, you still need to consider the conditions of your site as well as the natural range and habitat of the species you are considering. Where conditions are unfavourable, the choice is more limited, though many tree species will tolerate certain adverse conditions. If your soil is poor, you should discuss your choice of trees with your plant supplier. It is well worthwhile visiting other woods in your locality to see which tree species are

These young ash trees, growing in transplant lines in a nursery in summer, will be ready for lifting and sale in the autumn.

Most trees will grow on most sites – but in a productive woodland, you want the trees to grow vigorously, so careful species selection will pay dividends.

growing well. However, valid comparisons can only be made with sites with similar environmental conditions.

Where the intention is to work a woodland on a coppice cycle, the best species to use are sycamore, wild cherry, sweet chestnut, hornbeam or hazel, depending on the soil and climate of your site. Many other native broadleaved trees are suitable, but willow, alder and poplar are less suitable for firewood production, and beech and birch make poor coppice (although they are good for firewood). Ash was formerly recommended, but planting it is not currently advisable because of the problem of ash dieback. At this point no information is available on whether it is advisable to use wood from diseased ash trees for firewood, or on whether it can be stored successfully.

Sycamore is increasingly being recommended by the Forestry Commission. It has rapid regenerative properties – highly desirable if you are growing wood for fuel; it produces superior, clean-burning firewood which is quick to season, and it provides insect biomass for bats and birds.

In general terms, conifers are less suitable for firewood production, though slow-grown coniferous wood, from upland or northerly areas, makes better firewood than trees grown in sheltered lowland areas. Coniferous wood takes longer to dry, so you will need more storage space, and you need to be prepared to wait longer – up to three years – to have wood ready for burning. Wood from conifers makes good kindling, but it tends to spit and throw sparks, and it deposits resinous residues on the insides of chimneys and liners. This is a common cause of chimney fires.

Native broadleaved trees are the best option if you want your woodland to have landscape and ecological value in addition to its productive benefits. You could, however, choose to plant some conifers within your woodland as a 'nurse' crop, to provide shelter for the broadleaved saplings in the early stages. These could give you a cash crop of Christmas trees when they are thinned out.

Depending on your objectives, you may choose to grow a mixture of broadleaved species, or only one or two. If you want your woodland to have aesthetic and wildlife value, a mixture is preferable, as this looks far better in the landscape and contributes to biodiversity. However, if your only aim is to produce wood for fuel, it is better to plant just one or two species for ease of management. If you are planting two species, you can plant in alternate rows or in alternate pairs or triplets within the rows. The latter is preferable if the site is visible in the landscape.

Woodlands composed of a single species have been popular in the past as they make management easier. However, single-species planting has a negative effect on biodiversity, and single-species woodlands, especially those where all the trees are the same age, are vulnerable to pests and diseases, climate changes and natural hazards such as storms.

Recommended firewood species

Native broadleaves

Alder	Fair	Needs to be very dry. Spits and sparks profusely.
Apple	Good	Has a pleasant smell.
Beech	Excellent	Lasts well, if seasoned.
Birch	Very good	Emits considerable heat. Rots quickly in a woodpile, so needs to be kept very dry.
Elm	Excellent	Slow-burning. Needs to be well seasoned.
Field maple	Good	Calorific and clean-burning.
Hawthorn	Excellent	Emits good heat, lasts well.
Hazel	Very good	Emits good heat.
Holly	Very good	Burns when green.
Hornbeam	Excellent	Emits a great deal of heat.
Oak	Excellent	Good for heat. Lasts well, but needs to be very well seasoned.
Pear	Good	Has a pleasant smell.
Sweet chestnut	Good	Sparks and spits profusely.
Sycamore	Good	Quick to season. Clean-burning and good for heat.
Wild cherry	Excellent	Slow to season in the round due to its very thick bark, so should be split while green.

Conifers

Cedar	Excellent	Burns well and does not spit much for a conifer.
Cypress/ Western red cedar	Good	Burns well but produces plenty of sparks.
Larch	Fair	Burns well, but throws sparks explosively.
Pine	Good	Burns well, but prone to sparking and very sooty.

Ornamental tree species like redwood and cedar do make good firewood, but they are not suitable for inclusion in a native woodland.

Wherever possible, it is best to plant native species of local provenance. You should always avoid planting invasive non-native species. If you are planting new woodland alongside existing ancient woodland, you need to give especially careful consideration to species selection and genetic provenance.

Ornamental trees suitable for firewood

Bay *Laurus nobilis*
False acacia *Robinia pseudoacacia*
Gum *Eucalyptus* spp.
Hickory *Carya ovata*
Mesquite *Prosopis* spp.
Plane *Platanus hispanica*
Walnut *Juglans regia*

Many of these species can be found growing on private estates and in large gardens, as well as in public parks, botanical gardens and open spaces. Wood from these trees can often be obtained following storm damage, and can be used to supplement your log supply – or you may wish to plant ornamental tree species in your own garden. They should not, however, be planted within a native woodland, because they could upset the ecology.

Tree spacing

Whatever type of woodland layout you choose (see Chapter 2), having regular spacings between the trees makes management easier. When the trees are small, it also helps you to find them! Regular spacing is also better for mechanised work. However, random spacing in and/or between rows is preferred if a more natural appearance is desired or if wildlife habitat creation and conservation are primary objectives. Variable spacing also allows space for natural regeneration to supplement the planted trees.

The planting distance between the trees depends on the species and on the management system you intend to follow. If you are opting for a coppice system, a greater planting density is recommended, as this will lead to increased competition for light, producing taller, straighter pole growth. Dense planting also speeds up 'canopy closure'. This is when the tree canopy meets, excluding light to competing ground growth such as grass and weeds. This is useful on weedy sites to keep maintenance costs down.

The recommended planting density for establishing new broadleaved coppice woodland is around 2,500 trees per hectare, which is equivalent to 2 by 2m spacing. This provides reasonably rapid canopy closure. This is then thinned to leave approximately 1,000 trees per hectare for coppicing, or 250 trees per hectare if they are to be grown to maturity and then felled.

If you intend to use machinery to manage your woodland, it may be better to use a closer spacing within the rows and wider spacing between the rows, so that machinery can operate between the trees in at least one direction. The spacing needs to reflect the size of the machinery to be used. Close spacing will only allow access for small machinery mounted on horticultural tractors or farm bikes. If you want to use normal agricultural equipment, you will need to plant at 3m spacing. A good compromise is to plant at 3m between the rows but closer within the rows.

3 x 3m spacing = 1,111 trees per hectare
2.5 x 2.5m spacing = 1,600 trees per hectare
2 x 2m spacing = 2,500 trees per hectare

Matrix planting

A suggested method for deciding how many trees of each species you will plant is to draw up a matrix of approximately 10 by 10m. Two examples are shown.

See sample plant matrixes:

A: for trees and shrubs at 2 x 2m spacings

B: for trees and shrubs at 3 x 1.5m spacings, to allow for the use of machinery

C: for trees and shrubs at 1 x 1m spacings, for woodland edge

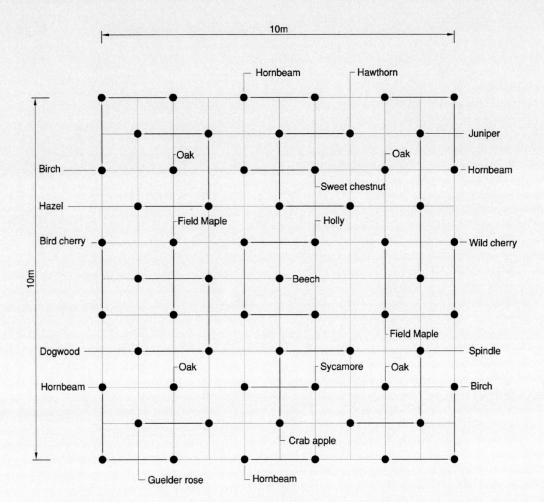

10m

10m

- Hornbeam
- Hawthorn
- Juniper
Birch
- Oak
- Oak
- Hornbeam
Hazel
- Sweet chestnut
Bird cherry
- Field Maple
- Holly
- Wild cherry
- Beech
- Field Maple
Dogwood
- Spindle
- Oak
- Sycamore
- Oak
Hornbeam
- Birch
- Crab apple
- Guelder rose
- Hornbeam

**Matrix design (A)
for trees and shrubs
at 2 x 2m spacings**

Botanical Name	Common Name	Qty
Canopy Tree Layer		
Acer campestre	Field maple	4
Acer pseudoplatanus	Sycamore	2
Betula pendula	Silver birch	6
Carpinus betulus	Hornbeam	10
Castanea sativa	Sweet chestnut	2
Fagus sylvatica	Beech	1
Quercus robur	Common oak	4
Secondary Tree Layer		
Ilex aquifolium	Holly	4
Malus sylvestris	Crab apple	3
Prunus avium	Wild cherry	2
Prunus padus	Bird-cherry	2
Shrub Layer		
Cornus sanguinea	Dogwood	4
Corylus avellana	Hazel	4
Crataegus monogyna	Hawthorn	4
Euonymus europaeus	Spindle-tree	3
Juniperus communis	Juniper	
Viburnum opulus	Guelder rose	2

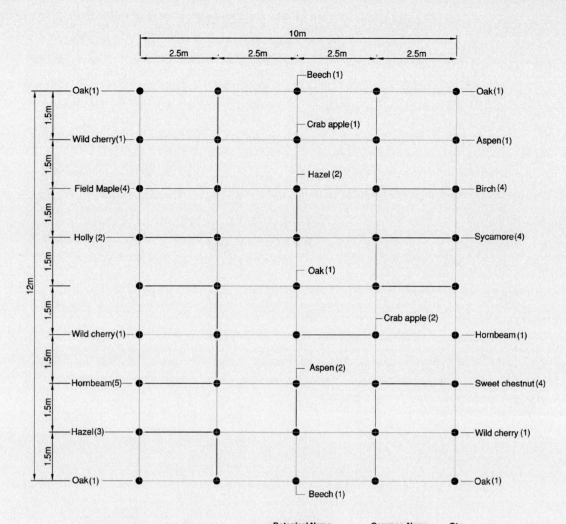

**Matrix design (B)
for trees and shrubs
at 3 x 1.5m spacings**

Botanical Name	Common Name	Qty
Canopy Tree Layer		
Acer Campestre	Field maple	4
Acer pseudoplatanus	Sycamore	4
Betula pendula	Birch	4
Castanea sativa	Sweet chestnut	4
Fagus sylvatica	Beech	2
Quercus robur	Oak	5
Secondary Tree Layer		
Carpinus betulus	Hornbeam	6
Ilex aquifolium	Holly	2
Malus sylvestris	Crab apple	3
Populus tremula	Aspen	3
Prunus avium	Wild cherry	3
Shrub Layer		
Corylus avellana	Hazel	5
Total		45

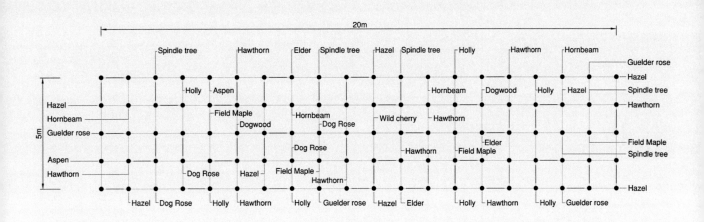

Botanical Name	Common Name	Qty
Trees		
Acer campestre	Field maple	4
Carpinus betulus	Hornbeam	4
Populus tremula	Aspen	2
Prunus avium	Wild cherry	1

Botanical Name	Common Name	Qty
Shrubs		
Cornus sanguinea	Dogwood	5
Corylus avellana	Hazel	21
Crataegus monogyna	Hawthorn	19
Euonymus monogyna	Spindle tree	10
Ilex aquifolium	Holly	13
Rosa canina	Dog rose	5
Sambucus nigra	Elder	9
Viburnum opulus	Guelder rose	7
Total		100

Matrix design (C)
for trees and shrubs at 1 x 1m
spacings for woodland edge

Implementation

4 STOCK

Now that the design of your woodland is taking shape, there are decisions to be made about the type of tree stock to plant.

YOUNG TREES ARE SOLD in a choice of sizes and forms, which include bare-root transplants, cell-grown trees, whips and standards. It is generally better to opt for planting smaller trees, as these have a better survival rate. Smaller trees also grow much more quickly and can overtake larger plants in as little as three years.

Ensure that the stock you buy is of high quality, and return any substandard trees; planting them is a waste of time and money. Ideally, visit the tree nursery to inspect the stock before buying it. Check that shoots and buds are healthy, and look for any evidence of fungal growth, insect pests and scarred bark.

Most nurseries sell stock by height, but more important is the diameter of the stem where it meets the roots (root collar diameter). A sturdy stem generally indicates a healthy root system. British Standard 3936: Part 4: 1984 specifies minimum root collar diameters for a range of species, and you should check that your planting stock meets these requirements.

Bare-root transplants

These vary in height between 15 and 60cm, and are priced accordingly. Transplants are grown in a nursery as seedlings and are then undercut annually to encourage the development of a fibrous root system and a good root:shoot ratio. This produces a plant which will cope well with transplanting. A bare-root transplant that has spent two years in a seed-bed followed by one year in a transplant bed is described as a '2+1' in nursery catalogues.

Bare-root trees should be sealed in special double-sided black/white planting bags when they are lifted. This ensures the least possible shock to the tree between lifting and replanting. Bare-root stock can be planted between November and the end of March.

ADVANTAGES: Cheapest and most widely available type of stock.

DISADVANTAGES: Need to be handled carefully to prevent drying out. Usually imported from Europe on the wholesale market, so difficult to source from UK provenance.

Cell-grown trees

These vary in age and in the length of time they have been hardened off, and are available in sizes ranging from 15 to 50cm. They are grown from seed in plastic or paper cells, so have a completely intact fibrous root system within a growing medium. Cell-grown trees are started off in polytunnels and then hardened off outside. They should be moved outside by late August, and you should be wary of cell-grown stock still under cover after this point. They can be planted from October through to May.

Cell-grown stock used to be significantly more expensive than bare-root stock, but the gap has closed in recent years, making cell-grown trees an increasingly attractive option.

ADVANTAGES: More resistant to drying out. Less prone to handling damage. Can be stored for longer before planting. Superior root:shoot ratio. More vigorous establishment. Easy to source from UK provenance.

DISADVANTAGES: Slightly more expensive.

Whips, feathered whips and standards

These are larger trees ranging from 90cm (whips and feathered whips) to 3m (standards). They can be purchased bare-rooted at the smaller sizes, or with soil attached. However, they are usually unsuitable for woodland creation.

ADVANTAGES: Good for situations where an instant effect and low numbers are required.

DISADVANTAGES: More expensive. More difficult to move and plant. There is a higher rate of loss (up to 40%). Those that do survive often have their growth and vigour permanently stunted.

Trees from seed

A longer-term option is to gather ripe or newly fallen seed from existing trees. Sow it immediately, either where you want the trees to grow, or in a seed-bed. Sow many more seeds than you want trees, as there will be losses to pests and weather. If you have sown the trees in a seed-bed, they can be transplanted once they are around 60cm high. If you have sown *in situ*, thin them as necessary to leave the best saplings to grow on.

Self-seeded trees

You can also look out for naturally occurring tree seedlings on your land. If they are growing in a suitable position, remove the competing vegetation, furnish them with a tree shelter, and allow them to grow on.

These self-seeded sycamores are growing beneath the canopy of established trees.

Care of stock

Proper care of new tree stock is vital to minimise losses. Between leaving the nursery and being planted in their final positions, damage to the trees can occur in four ways:

- Roots can dry out due to exposure to climatic conditions, especially drying winds. Twenty minutes' exposure to a drying wind is enough to kill or permanently stunt the growth of bare-rooted stock, so buy from a reputable supplier and keep it covered up until you are ready to plant it. Roots can also be damaged by extreme temperatures.

- Plants can suffer in very high temperatures, particularly if they are in bundles or if the foliage is wet. Keep them in the shade, even when the plants are in a paper bag, and especially if they are in a black plastic bag.

- Rough handling can damage branches and roots, especially when trees are being unloaded. Handle them with care, and keep them covered and protected at all times.

- Trees should be replanted as soon as possible. If they must be stored before planting, they should be removed from their packaging and heeled into a rooting medium, ensuring that all the roots are covered. Do not leave trees soaking in a bucket of water for longer than half an hour.

Left to right:

Bare-root stock should be sold in special double-sided planting bags to protect the roots between lifting and transplanting.

Careless handling of young trees will cause damage and can easily kill them.

Aim to minimise the time young trees spend out of the ground. Ideally, do not buy them until you are ready to plant.

5 | SITE GROUNDWORK

Preparing the planting site carefully will ensure that your young trees are given the best possible start.

Ground preparation

Careful preparation of the planting site will improve your success rate and reduce the need for maintenance and tree replacement. The best time for this job is in autumn, assuming that climatic conditions are suitable. It should only be done when the soil is dry enough to allow machinery on to the site without compacting the soil.

Former arable fields are suitable for woodland creation, though the weed seed bank in the soil can be a problem.

The aim of ground preparation is to improve soil drainage and structure and decrease competition for light, water and nutrients. Check if there are any factors likely to impede growth, such as compacted soil, very heavy clay soil or poor drainage, by digging soil pits at intervals across the site. Look out for grey/blue mottling of the soil and a sour smell. This indicates that the soil is periodically waterlogged or that drainage is impeded, and that you should choose tree species adapted to wet soil. Break up compacted or very heavy soils mechanically, using a mole-plough or cultivator. Perennial weeds such as bindweed, docks and thistles should be eradicated, using a weedkiller or by hand.

Avoid the temptation to make soil amendments. There should be no need to add fertilisers or manures. If the site shows nutrient deficiencies, an effective option is to include alder in the planting mix, as this species is a nitrogen-fixer, capturing atmospheric nitrogen and returning it to the soil as its leaves fall and decompose.

Pasture

All kinds of pasture are suitable for the establishment of trees, provided that the grass around the base of each tree is removed. The easiest option is to plant straight into the existing

Fields which have been grazed are ideal for new woodland, as the established sward makes management much easier.

grassland, killing the grass around the base of each tree using a herbicide or mulch. Spraying the whole area might seem like less effort, but the creation of an expanse of browned grass and the overuse of chemicals are best avoided. It is also likely to lead to subsequent weed problems. Large areas of long and overgrown grass will need to be removed by machinery and stockpiled to rot down.

However, established grassland often has small populations of voles. Be aware that removing livestock or stopping a cutting or mowing regime can result in a vole population explosion that could put young trees at risk. Keeping nearby grass short in the early years of a woodland will deprive them of cover and let predators spot them more easily.

Alternatively, you may wish to plough the site and then reseed it with a low-productivity grass or grass/wildflower mix. Reseeding has the advantage of letting you know exactly what grass mix is present, and therefore how to control it, and it reduces colonisation by weeds. It is essential to use a low-vigour grass mix. Many suppliers sell specific grass mixes for forestry.

Planting trees on grassland is generally easier than planting on arable land, where competing weeds can be a serious problem. Grass is easy to control immediately around the trees, and the remaining sward will exclude weeds.

Arable land

Former arable fields can be left as stubble before tree-planting takes place. The ruts and uneven surfaces of stubble can actually be beneficial because they provide localised shelter which can aid establishment – although they can also allow weeds to colonise the site and make their control more difficult.

Ex-arable sites may have a plough pan, or other soil compaction problems, that could restrict root development. A plough pan is a layer of consolidated soil minerals which forms just below the depth of previous cultivation and is impenetrable

Opposite:
The only ground preparation needed here is to create planting sites by killing the grass over an area of 1m in diameter where each tree will go. The remaining sward can be left to grow on.

to tree roots. It may be necessary to subsoil the field to relieve compaction. Avoid planting into the rip lines left by a subsoiler, however, because although this makes the planting quick and easy, the cracks created by the subsoiler tine can burst open in a dry year, leaving the trees vulnerable to drought.

Ploughing arable fields before planting trees should be avoided unless the soil is extremely compacted, as this will stimulate rapid weed growth. Arable soils have a large weed seed bank, and on fertile sites weeds can grow rapidly and will need to be controlled by the use of herbicides or suppressed by other vegetation.

An existing copse between arable fields could become the basis for a new woodland with new planting in one of the fields.

Scrub

If your planting site has been invaded by scrub, you can either clear this or cut openings into it in which to plant the trees. Unwanted regeneration of scrubby growth can be prevented by a topical application of systemic herbicide on to the freshly cut stumps (within 20 minutes of making the cut).

Marking out

Marking out the planting area is done for two reasons. The first is to locate the boundaries of the planting, and the second is to ensure that the plants are set out correctly, in line with the possible layouts described in the previous chapter.

The following methods can be used:

Full grid

This requires a grid to be marked out at the required spacing both up and down and across the planting area. This can be undertaken using a bar attached to the back of a tractor, or with a subsoiler.

Half grid

This is the same as a full grid, but marking is in one direction only. It is used on steep terrain or where a more simplified management regime can be implemented. Planting poles can be used to mark the distances of plants within the rows.

Poles & string

This involves marking out the planting area with poles and indicating the rows with string. Marked planting poles are used to establish the distance between the rows.

Canes

This is the easiest, quickest and cheapest method, but has the greatest room for error. The area is marked out with rods or canes, which means that the distance between rows and within rows can vary. It is not ideal on sites where any mechanised tools will be used. It can be used for small areas of planting, especially irregular areas, and on steep slopes.

6 PLANTING

The best way to plant your trees depends on the scale of your woodland – but whichever method you choose, care is key to successful establishment.

Timing

All trees should be planted while they are dormant. While the tree-planting season is usually from October to March, it is best to avoid the period from the end of December to mid-February unless the weather is especially mild.

Notch planting is commonly used for large-scale forestry planting. Both small bare-rooted trees and cell-grown stock can be notch-planted.

Photo: Woodland Trust

Methods

There are two main planting methods: notch-planting and pit-planting.

Notch-planting

This is the quickest and cheapest method when using small bare-rooted stock. Slits are cut in the ground and held open with the spade while the roots are carefully inserted so that they spread downwards. The ground is then gently firmed around the tree while the plant is pulled upwards so that the original root collar is at ground level.

With cell-grown stock, a crowbar can be used to make holes for planting.

ADVANTAGES: Fast. With practice and attention to detail, it can be effective.

DISADVANTAGES: Because it is fast, the quality of planting can suffer, and root growth can be impeded.

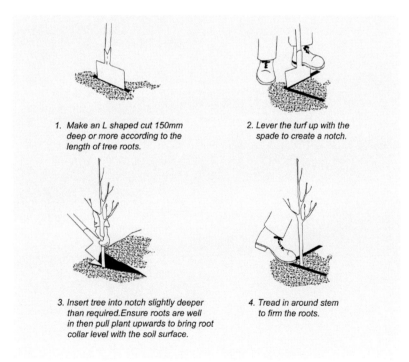

1. Make an L shaped cut 150mm deep or more according to the length of tree roots.

2. Lever the turf up with the spade to create a notch.

3. Insert tree into notch slightly deeper than required. Ensure roots are well in then pull plant upwards to bring root collar level with the soil surface.

4. Tread in around stem to firm the roots.

Pit-planting

This involves digging a hole a little wider and deeper than the roots of the tree. You then place the tree in the hole with the original soil mark at ground level. The roots should be spread evenly in the pit. A small mound of soil in the bottom of the hole will aid an even spread. If the soil is heavy clay, the bottom of the hole should be broken up. Soil should then be placed around the roots while you gently shake the tree to allow soil to sift into the root system, preventing air pockets. The soil should be firmed in layers as filling proceeds. Firm heavier soils lightly and light soils firmly.

ADVANTAGES: Takes better care of the roots. Good for smaller plantings or when tree planters are inexperienced.

DISADVANTAGES: Much slower.

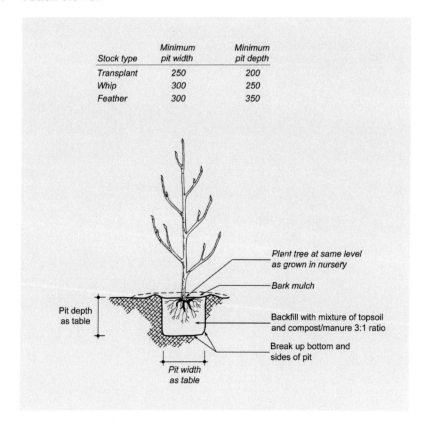

Stock type	Minimum pit width	Minimum pit depth
Transplant	250	200
Whip	300	250
Feather	300	350

Plant tree at same level as grown in nursery

Bark mulch

Backfill with mixture of topsoil and compost/manure 3:1 ratio

Break up bottom and sides of pit

Pit depth as table

Pit width as table

Pit-planting, the technique being used here, takes better care of the roots, but is more time-consuming.

Soil improvers

There is rarely any need to add any growing medium to the soil at the time of planting, and on most lowland sites fertiliser is not required.

Staking

Stakes should only be used with standard-size trees, unless it is necessary because the site is particularly exposed or subject to harsh weather. Check newly planted trees regularly, however, to ensure that they remain well firmed into the ground.

Management

7 | PROTECTION

Newly planted trees are vulnerable to a range of hazards – but careful protection should see them safely through their first few years.

ONE ADVANTAGE OF WOODLAND is that it requires far less attention than other land uses. However, newly planted trees cannot be expected to thrive on their own. Woodlands must be actively managed until the young trees are strong enough to hold their own against grazing animals, weeds and weather.

Guards & shelters

Enclosing each newly planted tree within an individual guard or shelter gives it a considerable degree of protection. Tree guards provide a physical barrier to protect against damage by mammals, and the shelters also enhance growth through a 'greenhouse' effect. Shelters benefit most species, and can dramatically improve survival and growth rates. Some species

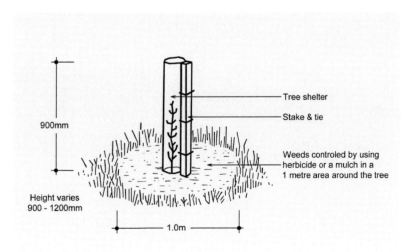

900mm

Height varies
900 - 1200mm

1.0m

Tree shelter

Stake & tie

Weeds controled by using
herbicide or a mulch in a
1 metre area around the tree

Photo: Woodland Trust

can be expected to more than double their growth rate in the first few years if provided with a shelter. Guards and shelters also clearly mark tree locations, making them easier to find and manage in the early stages.

Many types of guards and shelters are available, in a wide range of shapes, sizes and materials. Spiral guards prevent bark stripping by rabbits and hares. Mesh guards protect young trees from bark stripping and browsing, and also enhance growth by providing a sheltered environment. Solid polypropylene or polyethylene shelters provide the greatest enhancement to growth and are the most popular choice. These translucent plastic tubes assist establishment by providing a warm microclimate and reducing moisture stress – though they can encourage spindly growth. They also give a degree of protection against damage by herbicides and machinery.

Guards and shelters need to be secured to stout wooden stakes by means of clips or wire. Most types are designed to break down after five to ten years, so it is then necessary to remove the debris. If the plastic has not broken down, the shelters will need to be taken off by hand.

Animal control

Grazing, whether by wild animals such as deer and rabbits, or by farm livestock such as sheep, can damage or kill young trees, so some form of protection is essential. Damage can be prevented by protecting the trees individually with guards or shelters, by fencing the woodland area, or by controlling the populations of pest species.

Fitting your young trees with guards or shelters will afford them the greatest protection, provided the type you choose is proof against the animal(s) likely to be a problem. As well as ensuring that their design is effective against the animal(s) in question, it is vital that you fit guards of sufficient height. If animals can reach the top of the guards, the trees will simply be browsed off every time they reach that height.

One major advantage of protecting each tree individually is that if a guard or shelter is damaged, only that tree is put at risk. Fitting individual shelters is generally more economical than fencing on areas of less than 2ha (5 acres), or where the woodland is irregular in shape. However, many guards and shelters do not protect against vole damage, and squirrels may also breach them. Small pests can, in fact, be encouraged by tree shelters, which provide good nest sites.

For areas of more than 2ha, erecting fencing around the whole woodland can be significantly cheaper than fitting individual guards or shelters. Fencing can be less obtrusive in the landscape, and also serves to restrict unwanted public access. However, it is more expensive than guards or shelters on small sites, and if a fence is breached, all the trees are immediately vulnerable.

Farm livestock

If sheep have access to the woodland, 1.8m shelters can be used to protect the trees, provided that the shelters are very firmly staked. Alternatively, use a standard stock fence to exclude farm livestock from the woodland. For cattle and horses, a buffer zone is needed between the fence and the trees.

Deer

Deer are an increasing problem in most areas of the country. Where they are present it is impossible to establish new trees, or achieve regrowth on coppiced trees, without fencing or other protection.

This fencing is not of sufficient height to exclude deer, and should be increased to 1.8 to 2m to fully protect the trees. Adding strands of wire, especially barbed wire, can result in serious injuries to deer who fail to jump over and face a lingering death if caught on the wires.

Netting or mesh fences are necessary to exclude deer, as they can push through wire fences. Deer can injure themselves if they attempt to jump normal stock fences, particularly those with barbed wire along the top, so properly constructed deer fencing of the correct height is essential. A height of 2m is needed to exclude the larger species (red, sika and fallow) and 1.5m for roe and muntjac. Muntjacs can push under netting, so where they are present the fencing will need to be lapped or buried, as for rabbits.

Electric fencing can be an effective temporary option against deer. Easily moveable fencing systems are useful for coppice management, so the fence can be relocated to protect each newly cut coupe.

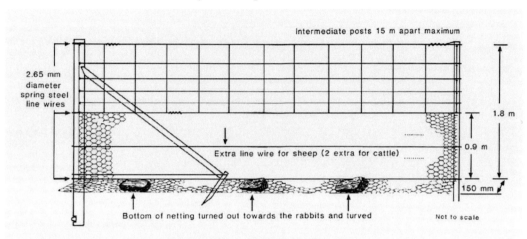

Tree guards can be used to protect against deer, but they must be of sufficient height and robust enough to resist damage. 1.8m high guards are available for protection against the larger species.

Dead-hedging, where you create barriers from prunings and brushwood, can be a viable method of protecting coppice from deer (except muntjac, which can push through it). Dead-hedging can be constructed using the small-diameter waste material from coppicing, so is a cheap and efficient option. Well-constructed dead-hedging will last long enough to protect the regrowth, and then rot down *in situ*. It will also provide a valuable habitat for wildlife.

Rabbits & hares

Rabbits can be a serious pest in new woodlands, particularly on ex-agricultural land, where numbers are often high. Newly planted trees are vulnerable to rabbits browsing the leaves and shoots and stripping the bark. Damage is most severe in winter

Competing vegetation within a 50cm radius of each young tree must be removed completely, with a chemical herbicide, by mulching, by hand or by machinery. The best method depends on the size of the woodland. It is not sufficient to cut or mow grass around the trees as this will make the situation worse by encouraging the growth of the sward. Grass-mowing machinery can also inflict considerable damage on young trees.

Chemicals

Herbicides are the most effective method of weed control, but they can be costly, and spraying has to be done with considerable care. It is best done when trees are not in leaf. Do not spray within 5cm of the base of the trunk, even if this means missing a few weeds. As with any chemical, it is essential to use the correct equipment and to follow the instructions carefully.

ADVANTAGES: Very effective if done properly and at the right time.

DISADVANTAGES: Expensive. Requires knowledge and training. Most trees require protection from sprays. Can damage trees and the wider environment if used incorrectly. Should be avoided near watercourses. Not suitable near evergreen trees.

Mulching

Mulching smothers weeds and prevents weed seeds from germinating. It takes many forms, but the most effective for the establishment period is to use specially made mulch mats of plastic sheeting or woven polypropylene. These are secured using various types of pins and pegs, or by digging in the edges.

Provided the ground has been cleared of all vegetation, mulch mats can be covered with wood chippings to a depth of approximately 50mm, over a

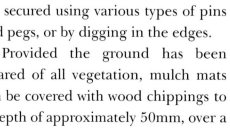

A wood chip mulch can provide good weed control, as long as it is topped up regularly.

Photo: Woodland Trust

minimum area of 1m in diameter around each tree. This can then be topped up as required. It is important to check the synthetic mat underneath regularly and enlarge the hole as necessary, as the tree can otherwise be strangled.

Here, straw bales are being used to smother the grass to create planting sites for trees.

Mulching using natural materials such as wood or bark chips can be done without the mats, and this is the most natural way of replicating a woodland leaf litter. It has the added environmental advantage of being 100% biodegradable. Organic mulches like straw or wood chippings are cheap, especially if you use waste materials from elsewhere on your property. Alternatively, you can source wood chips economically from your local tree surgeon.

ADVANTAGES: Can make chemical treatment unnecessary, so is more eco-friendly. Black plastic mulches raise the soil temperature, stimulating root growth. Organic mulches can be a cost-effective option.

DISADVANTAGES: More time-consuming than using chemicals. Organic mulches need topping up each season to remain effective, and mulch mats will eventually need replacing. Mulch mats can encourage pests, which nest underneath them. Mulching with bought-in materials can be more expensive than using herbicides.

Mechanical weeding

This is the cutting of vegetation with a mower, strimmer or tractor-mounted swipe. This is rarely a good option; in fact, long grass is less of a competing environment than short, regularly mown grass.

If you intend to use machinery for weed control, this needs to be planned into the design, as you will need 3m between the rows for access.

On small areas, hoeing, taking care not to damage the trees, is an effective option, but it is labour-intensive and needs to be done every few weeks through the growing season.

ADVANTAGES: Low-cost and requires no special skills.

DISADVANTAGES: Needs to be done several times a year. Easy to get too close to the trees and damage them, especially when using a strimmer. Most weed species survive mowing or cutting, and with aggressive grass species, mowing can encourage faster growth. Needs to be timed to minimise disruption to ground-nesting birds.

Benefits of weed control

- Eliminates competition for limited soil moisture
- Maximises the amount of rainfall percolating into the soil
- Increases soil temperature in spring, promoting early root growth
- Reduces competition for nutrients
- Contributes to the supply of nutrients as dead weeds decompose
- Stops trees being shaded or swamped by competing growth
- Discourages voles from damaging trees
- Minimises weed seed production and consequent problems elsewhere on your property

Woodland floor

If you also want your woodland to be a landscape amenity, the sward of wild flowers and grasses should be retained in all areas left vacant after planting, except for the 1m diameter areas around each tree described above. Some woodland floor plants will not succeed when the canopy grows larger and creates more shade, but if thinning of the trees and coppicing is undertaken, they may return.

A woodland floor can be rich in plant life while the trees are young or newly coppiced.

8 MAINTENANCE

Regular attention to maintenance is essential to ensure that your young trees survive and thrive.

THE FIRST FIVE YEARS ARE CRUCIAL for establishing trees. During this time they are vulnerable to competition for light, nutrients and water, as well as to grazing by many animals. There will inevitably be casualties, and replacing trees that have died in the first few years after planting is known as 'beating up'. However, careful maintenance will keep losses to a minimum.

Weeding

The removal of weeds around the new trees is essential. This can be achieved by the careful use of chemicals, or by the other methods described in the previous chapter. It is especially important to control any invasive plants in a new woodland, such as rhododendron, laurel, Himalayan balsam, Japanese knotweed, periwinkle and bamboo.

Watering

If there is a prolonged dry period in the two years after planting, it may be necessary to water young trees. If they show any signs of wilting, apply 90 litres (20 gallons) of water gradually around each tree, allowing it to soak into the soil.

Feeding

On most woodland sites fertiliser is not required. Trees benefit most from a healthy nutrient cycle of fallen leaves and twigs. The use of fertilisers, slurry and manure can be very damaging, not only to the trees but to the symbiotic relationship that trees have with fungi.

Pruning off the lower branches will produce a straighter, more valuable trunk.

Pruning

The most valuable trees for timber are those where the trunk is perfectly straight and branch-free. To achieve this, unwanted low-growing branches need to be removed with secateurs while they are very small, or with a saw or loppers. Even if your main aim is to produce firewood, you could choose to manage some of your trees in this way and allow them to grow to maturity, producing a valuable final crop for which your descendants will be grateful. Such selected trees are known as 'standards', and 'coppice with standards' has been the most popular management method for woodland since medieval times.

The earlier unwanted branches are removed, the more 'clear', knot-free timber you will produce. However, if too many live branches are removed, the reduction of leaf area will cause the growth rate of the tree to slow. Pruning should concentrate on removing dead branches and those contributing little to tree growth at the bottom of the crown.

The best time for pruning is in spring, when growth is active. Cut off unwanted branches at a point just beyond the swelling of the trunk around their base. Neat pruning close to the stem is vital; leaving a jagged stump can lead to infection, or to the development of a tear down the tree stem. With larger branches, it is best to remove the weight of the branch first, before making a clean second cut close to the trunk. This helps to avoid tearing the bark below the cut.

Pruning is time-consuming, and it is only essential if branches are dead, damaged, diseased or dangerous, or if you want to harvest good-quality timber from particular trees. Routine pruning is not necessary if you are only harvesting your trees for firewood, especially if you are managing your woodland on a coppice system.

Thinning

Trees are usually planted close together in order to shade out competing vegetation quickly, and to encourage them to grow straight and tall. However, once their canopy meets, they start to affect one another's growth, competing for light, water and nutrients. This is the point at which thinning becomes beneficial.

Thinning removes the less healthy or less desirable trees, giving the remainder more space and light to develop. If you planted a 'nurse' species, such as a conifer or a fast-growing

Photo: The National Forest

This young woodland has reached the point at which trees should be selected for thinning.

Photo: The National Forest

Now that this woodland has been thinned, the surviving trees have more space to grow, and the increased light means that the lower layers of the woodland can develop.

broadleaf like wild cherry, to provide protection to the main species in their early stages, this should now be removed. Thinning will give you a harvest of low-quality, small-diameter wood that can be used as firewood and for kindling.

Thinning is not necessary in the first ten years. It should then be carried out at regular intervals – usually every five to ten years, depending on the type of harvest required, for broadleaves, and every five years for conifers. You should time the operation to avoid the bird nesting season.

Thinning needs to be done with skill and care, as felled trees can become caught up in the crowns of the remaining trees, leading to potentially dangerous situations. Extraction of the felled trees must be done carefully to avoid damage to the bark of the remainder.

Here, selected trees have been left to become standards after coppicing and thinning have taken place.

Photo: Woodland Trust

Another method of thinning is to remove the larger trees; this gives you a more useful harvest and allows the sub-dominant trees to develop for the next thinning. This technique also admits light to the woodland floor, encouraging the lower layers of the woodland to develop. A third option is to thin the woodland in sections, removing just a few trees each year, as needed for firewood or for building projects.

Protective aids

Tree guards, shelters, stakes and ties should be checked regularly to ensure that they are intact and that they are not rubbing or damaging the trees. They should be removed as soon as the trees are well established. Too many trees are permanently damaged or even killed by the non-removal of these aids.

Open grown trees tend to have short main stems with long coarse side branches.
Conservation value high, timber value low.

Too close a spacing produces tall, spindly, unstable trees.
Conservation value low, timber value low.

Regular thinning allows selection of the best trees.
Conservation value moderate, timber value high.

Tree thinning

9 HARVESTING

Once your trees reach a useable size, there are several ways you can harvest them for firewood: by coppicing, by felling, or by using the wood from pruning, thinning or storm damage.

Coppicing

The technique of coppicing, widely used to manage trees in the past, is the best way of managing small woodlands where the main objective is to produce firewood, with the possibility of an additional small yield of poles suitable for fencing. The new growth from coppicing, known as 'underwood', has long been used for many purposes, and especially for fuel. As well as producing a much earlier harvest than felling, coppicing has the advantage of producing slim poles that are easy to handle manually and which can simply be cross-cut to produce logs for burning.

Coppicing is also the best management choice where time, labour and money are limited and the care of the woodland needs to be intermittent. Once the trees are established, labour input is low. A small crop can be expected at each coppicing, and working is concentrated as much as possible. Coppicing can actually be beneficial for trees, and trees that are coppiced tend to live longer.

The technique involves cutting broadleaved trees down to just above the ground, at regular intervals of between five and 25 years, depending on the species and its growth rate. A cluster of new shoots sprouts up from the stump or 'stool', and these grow into a crop of poles that can be cut again. Leaving a 10 to 15cm stool preserves the starch reserves of the tree and encourages more prolific regrowth.

The cut should have a sloping face to encourage the shedding of water and, if possible, should be south-facing to encourage drying. Hand tools were traditionally used for coppicing, but trials have shown no difference between such tools and chainsaws in terms of the quality of the regrowth; the critical factor is that the cut is clean.

This newly coppiced tree has been cut at an angle to ensure water run-off. The stump will require protection from deer and other animals during the initial period of regrowth. Surrounding the stump with brushwood can keep deer away, but not squirrels and rabbits.

Photo: The National Forest

Coppicing should be done during the winter months, when the trees are dormant and the sap is 'down'. This is better for the health of the trees; it also means that there is less sap in the wood, so it needs less time to dry. The trees start to resprout the following spring, and will grow rapidly as their root system is already established.

Coppicing is done in blocks (known as coupes, cants or compartments) on a rotational cycle, with one coupe being cut each year. The size of the coupes and the length of the cycle are worked out so that by the time you return to the first coupe, it is ready for recutting. The best strategy is to grow poles of 6 to 12m tall and 70 to 150mm diameter on a 6- to 15-year cycle. If you wish to cut trees over 150mm in diameter, you may need a felling licence, depending on the volume being cut.

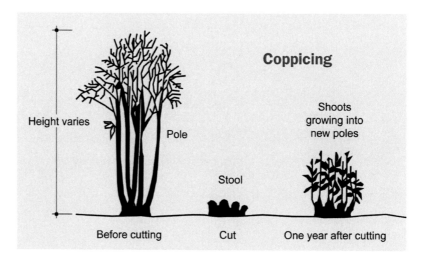

Coppicing

Height varies

Pole

Shoots growing into new poles

Stool

Before cutting   Cut   One year after cutting

To decide the size of your coupes, take the total area to be coppiced and divide it by the number of years that your chosen species needs between cuts.

Example: $\dfrac{3ha\ (7.5\ acres)}{9\ years\ rotation}$ = *1/3ha (0.85 acres)*

The coupes should not be too small or the newly coppiced trees will be shaded by the regrowth in surrounding coupes. A rule of thumb is that coupes should be between 0.25 and 1ha in size, but take up not more than a fifth of the woodland apiece.

The first round of coppicing may yield irregular quantities of wood from one year to the next, and any shortfall in firewood requirements will need to be met from other sources until the coppice cycle is fully established.

Secure fencing is essential around coppiced woodland, as the tender new shoots are extremely vulnerable to browsing, especially by deer and rabbits. You can discourage browsing by dead-hedging, or by building wigwams of brushwood over the stools. Cutting larger coupes also helps to reduce damage. There is, however, no failsafe alternative to fencing.

Coppicing and its frequency have a great effect on the vegetation within a wood. If the coppice is left uncut for too long, it does not admit sufficient light to support more than a

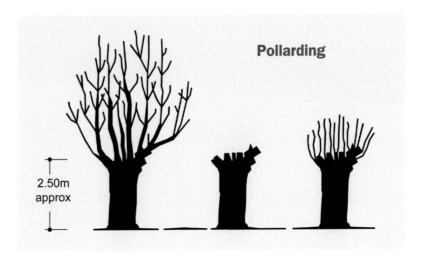

Pollarding

2.50m
approx

few of the most shade-tolerant species, so the shrub layer dies off and the spring flowers and profuse summer vegetation of a properly coppiced woodland disappear. At the other extreme, a woodland that is frequently coppiced loses some of its characteristics due to increased light and reduced humidity.

A variant on coppice management is 'coppice with standards', where 'standard' or 'timber' trees – often oak or ash – are allowed to grow to maturity above the coppiced trees. Pollarding is a similar technique to coppicing, except that the trees are cut at a higher level – between 2 and 3m above the ground – in order to raise the young shoots above the reach of grazing animals.

Recently pollarded willow trees growing on the Somerset Levels, where pollarding is a tradition.

Felling

In this system, all the trees in a given area are cut down at the same time. The cleared land is then replanted with a new crop of tree seedlings. This approach is more usual in coniferous woodlands.

Trees should be felled in winter, when they are dormant. In a small wood, felling is normally done by hand, using a chainsaw. It is important to use the correct blade length for the size of the trees, and to ensure that it is properly sharpened. The direction in which the trees will fall should be worked out beforehand to make the felling safe and the extraction of the timber as simple as possible. Extraction methods and routes should also be worked out in advance.

These logs have been cut to cord size and are ready to be seasoned.

Pruning, thinning & storm damage

Pruning and thinning (see Chapter 8) will both yield a small harvest of wood. Some will only be suitable for use as kindling, but larger pieces can be cut into logs and used as firewood. If you thin a woodland in sections, this allows you to take a small crop each year.

Storm damage will also produce a harvest, both of fallen branches and of trees which are damaged and need to be cut down.

Cutting & splitting the wood

Once you have cut your coppice poles or felled your trees, you then need to saw them into small lengths, and split any thicker pieces lengthways. As well as providing logs of a convenient size for burning, this increases the available surface area for rapid drying. Also, it is far easier to split wood when it is green than after it has seasoned. There are now labour-saving devices on the market which will make the job easier, such as hydraulic log-splitters.

You also need to fracture the bark, as tree bark is almost waterproof and must not be left intact or the wood will not dry. An easy way to do this is to run a chainsaw lightly along the length of the log; the bark will then start to crack and soon begin to fall off. Larger logs will need more than one chainsaw cut.

Seasoning

Good drying or 'seasoning' of firewood is vital. Although there are small differences in heat energy between different tree species, which species you grow is actually less important in calorific terms than how well you dry the wood. Although there are some species, like ash and holly, that can be burned 'wet' or 'green', you should only do this as a stop-gap if you run out of seasoned logs. Wet wood produces less heat, so you will need to burn more, and it produces a lot of smoke, causing unnecessary air pollution. It also causes chimney fires and fouling of chimney liners.

The first essential is a good storage area. Ideally, this should be a shed or barn big enough both to accommodate the harvested wood prior to cutting and splitting it, and to allow you to do the job in comfort and under cover. A good wood store is a uniquely satisfying place to work, and a wonderful place to be!

Your wood store must be absolutely dry, with good ventilation allowing a through-flow of air. This can be achieved by having a door or window which can be opened on each side of the building. It is also good to have some airflow beneath the wood; the easiest way of achieving this is to stack the wood on old pallets.

Wood store essentials

- located near the house
- good access for vehicles
- big enough to hold two years' supply of logs
- sturdy and structurally sound
- strong roof
- protected from rain-laden winds
- well ventilated
- free-draining flooring with airflow underneath

You should organise your storage area into sections, so you have one area where you stack new green wood, another for wood in the process of drying, and another in which the wood is dried and ready for use. It is often helpful to have more than one storage area, with wood which is ready for use being moved to a store closer to the house.

Stack the wood in a way that allows air to circulate around it. There is no need to stack it very neatly, and you should aim for an efficient method of working which avoids the need to handle the wood more than once. Try to work at waist height to avoid strain on your back. Very small-size produce should be stacked separately for use as kindling.

Wood-burning stove manufacturers recommend that wood should be dried to 20% moisture content before it is used. On average, this will take a year. The rule of thumb for firewood from broadleaved species is that logs which are cut one winter should be stacked through the summer months for use the following winter – though this does vary by species. The key drying time is the warmer months, so logs cut in March will be as well seasoned the following winter as those cut the previous November. Coniferous logs are best given two summers to season. If you need wood to season more quickly, simply cut it into smaller pieces.

Traditionally firewood has been measured and sold by the 'cord', which is a tightly packed stack measuring 2.4 by 1.2 by 1.2m (8 by 4 by 4ft), or approximately 3.6m³. The cord is still the unit of measurement for firewood in some parts of Britain, and it is widely used in North America. 'Cord' is also used as another word for firewood, indicating small-diameter wood of relatively poor quality, while 'timber' is large-diameter, high-quality wood destined for use in construction.

This exemplary wood store is divided into bays, so that new wood can be stacked separately from wood that is ready for burning.

Seasoning times for broadleaved species

Very quick-drying:	willow, poplar, alder
Fairly quick-drying:	ash, birch, lime, wych elm, sycamore, maples, planes, hickory, hazel, walnut
Fairly slow-drying:	beech, robinia, cherry, apple, pear, hawthorn, blackthorn, holly, horse chestnut, sweet chestnut, red oak, laburnum, rowan
Very slow-drying:	English oak, holm oak, English elm, hornbeam, yew, box

Safety

Woodland work is dangerous unless you have the necessary skills, experience and training, and the safety considerations cannot be overemphasised. It is vital that you know how to handle a chainsaw and any other cutting equipment safely, that you maintain it properly, and that you use all the recommended safety clothing and equipment. You also need to learn how to fell trees and move logs safely.

If you do not have the necessary skills and experience, you must undertake suitable training courses before embarking on any woodland work. Even when you are fully trained, you should never work alone if you are using a chainsaw or handling heavy logs, in case of accident.

With suitable training and equipment, woodland work is well within the capabilities of a farmer or smallholder. However, an alternative is to hire contractors to undertake the skilled and hazardous aspects of the work.

10 EXISTING WOODS

If you already have a woodland on your property, you are some years ahead of the game – but there is work to be done to bring it into productive management.

Assessment

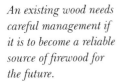

An existing wood needs careful management if it is to become a reliable source of firewood for the future.

The first step in bringing an existing woodland into productive management is to assess what is already there. If possible, it is helpful to do this over a full year. Assessing it in summer may give an overly favourable impression, particularly if drainage is an issue.

Start by surveying the woodland. Note site factors like altitude, aspect, exposure and soil type, the category and type

of woodland, the extent of the planted area(s), access to and within it, and the numbers, species, size and condition of the trees. Look for clues to past management practices, such as signs that the woodland has been coppiced. Make a note of any mature broadleaved trees, as these could be valuable for timber. You should also assess the structure of the woodland, noting the presence (or absence) and condition of each of the different layers (see Chapter 2). Note the open spaces in your woodland, whether there are rides or glades, and the condition of the woodland edges.

Because existing woodland will already be a habitat for wildlife, you should consider its ecological value in your plans. You should also weigh any loss of landscape amenity against your plans for productive management.

Once your survey is complete, make an annotated map or plan of your woodland. This can then form the basis for a Woodland Plan (see Chapter 1), which will indicate the best way of bringing your woodland into productive management.

If you do not have the necessary experience to survey your woodland and plan improvements, you should employ a professional to do this for you. You should also consult an expert if you have inherited a piece of ancient woodland (defined as having been continuously wooded for at least 400 years). This has immense historic and ecological value and needs to be managed with great sensitivity.

Access

If an existing woodland does not have access for vehicles, creating access may be a first step in bringing it into productive management. Harvesting timber without vehicular access can be very difficult.

Much of the flora and fauna in a wood occurs in the first 10m from the woodland edge, so if your woodland contains rides and glades, it is beneficial to preserve these rather than

You need to ensure – or create – good access into an established wood to allow for modern machinery.

filling them in with new planting. You may also wish to open up old rides and glades to allow more light into the wood. This has added practical benefits, improving access for working and creating off-road areas for the temporary stacking of harvested wood.

Felling

Felling and replanting can seem the obvious solution to poor quality woodland; however, most woodlands can be improved by other means. It is a costly option, either in money or in labour and time, and is only the best course of action if there are insufficient trees with harvesting potential, or if the woodland is overmature and shows little sign of regenerating

Cutting and felling operations are potentially dangerous and should only be undertaken after suitable training and with all the recommended safety clothing and equipment.

naturally. If you do undertake felling, it should be followed immediately by replanting, otherwise weeds can quickly colonise the site.

A good way of regenerating a woodland is group felling, where you fell groups of trees, creating openings which are then replanted or allowed to regenerate naturally. A new group is felled every few years. In this way a woodland can gradually be replaced without losing its landscape or wildlife value. However, if the woodland is small this can mean that the harvest is very low for many years.

Thinning

In old woodlands, broadleaved saplings frequently grow in dense thickets. As a first step, it is often necessary to cut swathes through the trees using a tractor and swipe, or with a chainsaw. Once it is possible to choose between individual trees, these should be thinned out to leave the best specimens space to mature. It may also be worthwhile pruning branches to improve the form of individual trees.

Thinning of a wood with more than one tree species has to be done with care because different species grow at different rates and slower-growing species may be lost unless they are given space to develop. Faster-growing but less desirable species may need to be removed.

In an existing woodland there will probably be a lot of dead wood and some fallen trees. Recently fallen wood can be collected, sawed into logs and used as firewood, but it is good to leave some dead and dying wood *in situ* for its wildlife value, as long as it poses no threat to people or property. Dead wood is not a threat to the health of the remaining trees.

Coppicing

Coppicing can be resumed after as many as 60 years of neglect, and is often the most successful way of bringing poor quality woodland back into management. However, it is not suitable for woods that have not been coppiced for a very long time, or

Coppicing is being reintroduced into this established wood, with a selection of the best trees retained as 'standards'.

Photo: Woodland Trust

that have never been coppiced. A survey of the woodland will help you decide on the pattern of coppicing and the length of coppice cycle most appropriate to the species in your wood.

If you want to leave some standard trees above your coppice, these will probably need to be thinned to allow more light to reach your coppiced trees. Adjacent areas of the woodland may also have to be thinned, or the coppiced trees will not have enough light to regrow well. For this reason, it is generally best to cut your first coupe on the edge of the woodland, or along the edge of a ride.

If you decide to coppice existing woodland, you must first fence the woodland to exclude grazing animals. Deer and rabbits in particular love to graze new coppice, and repeated browsing will kill even a large coppice stool within a few years.

New planting

Regenerating an existing woodland will almost certainly involve some new planting, either to fill in gaps where trees have died or been felled, or to extend the planted area. This provides an opportunity to add new species which will improve the productive value of the woodland. Note, however, that felling licence regulations prevent the conversion of broadleaved woodlands to coniferous woodlands, so if you have inherited a broadleaved woodland, you are limited to broadleaved species. Ideally you should opt for native broadleaved species of local provenance.

To give new trees enough light and moisture to grow, the planting area should be at least twice as wide as the height of the surrounding trees. New trees should always be planted outside the canopy of existing trees.

You can also encourage natural regeneration within a wood by clearing scrub to leave areas for colonisation by tree seedlings, and by clearing the ground around promising seedlings and equipping them with tree shelters.

Opposite:
There is sufficient space and light in this existing wood for additional trees to be planted.

Photo: Woodland Trust

Nothing can beat an open fire, not only for heating the house but as a place to sit on a cold night, whether socialising with friends – perhaps roasting chestnuts or heating mulled ale – or enjoying your own company, especially with the dog sleeping alongside.

CONCLUSION

PLANNING, DESIGNING, PLANTING AND MAINTAINING a woodland is an inspirational project, and woodland work can be one of the most enjoyable and rewarding aspects of managing a property. Trees are a long-term investment, so planting a woodland gives us a real stake in the future of the landscapes we are creating. A sustainable woodland is not only an amenity which will meet our present needs, but a legacy for future generations.

Creating a woodland is not something to be undertaken lightly. Establishing a successful, sustainable woodland does depend on thorough planning, thoughtful design, careful implementation and conscientious maintenance. If you are prepared to invest the necessary time, thought and care in the project, however, the rewards are immense.

Sustainable woodland management to provide firewood generates low-carbon energy and is also of huge benefit to wildlife and wild flower species, many of which are under threat. Coppice management is particularly beneficial, because its rotational system gives a woodland structural diversity and a variety of habitats which can support a wide range of flora and fauna.

Plan your woodland wisely and manage it well, and you should be harvesting your first firewood in ten years, and could be self-sufficient in fuel for heating within 20 years. Meanwhile, you will have the immense satisfaction of having created a wonderful landscape amenity, to be enjoyed now and in the future.

APPENDICES

Appendix 1. Legal issues

Tree felling laws

Most tree felling requires a felling licence from the Forestry Commission; contact your local office for details. There are, however, a number of exceptions.

You may fell up to 5m^3 each calendar quarter without a licence if not more than 2m^3 is sold. Trees with a diameter of less than 8cm at chest height are exempt from the regulations; this rises to 10cm if you are thinning, and 15cm if the stems are on a coppice stool.

Trees in gardens in the immediate surroundings of a house are also exempt, as are dead trees and those that pose an imminent hazard. No licence is required when the felling is done under the terms of a Forestry Commission grant scheme.

Some trees are covered by Tree Preservation Orders or are protected because they are in Conservation Areas or Sites of Special Scientific Interest (SSSIs). Check with your local authority tree officer or planning department before felling any established trees.

Transferring obligations

If you buy a wood, Forestry Commission grant schemes or felling licences may already be in place. Your solicitor should inform you of these.

In the case of a felling licence (including felling done under a grant scheme), the conditions go with the land and not with the owner. If your predecessor felled trees on the condition that new trees were planted and maintained for a given period, then you, as the new owner of the land, are responsible for maintaining the trees until the period is up.

Appendix 2. Grants

There are three schemes that provide farmers with annual payments to compensate for the agricultural income lost as a result of planting woodlands or making improvements to existing woodlands.

The Farm Woodland Scheme (FWS) and Farm Woodland Premium Scheme (FWPS) are now closed to new applicants, but existing agreements will continue as contracted until their expiry date. The administration of FWS and FWPS was transferred from Natural England to the Forestry Commission in 2007.

The English Woodland Grant Scheme (EWGS) opened in 2005. EWGS combines Woodland Creation Grants and Farm Woodland Payments in a single scheme. See **www.forestry.gov.uk** or contact your local Forestry Commission office for further details.

The Woodland Trust offers an alternative source of support through their MOREwoods scheme, which is suitable for small-scale or scattered planting sites. Find out more at **www.woodlandtrust.org.uk/firewood** or call **01476 452350**.

The government's Renewable Heat Incentive is available for domestic properties using a log-fired boiler system. It does not cover wood-burning stoves or open fires, and favours applicants who are not already on the gas grid.

Some county councils and local authorities have grant schemes and woodland advisers. Contact individual councils for details.

Grants may also be available to produce Woodland Plans. Currently there is a Woodland Planning Grant available from the Forestry Commission in England. Financial assistance may also be available from the Forestry Commission for ecological surveys of woodland.

Appendix 3. Woodland management plan

This Appendix is taken from the Small Woods Information Pack, available to members of the Small Woods Association **www.smallwoods.org.uk**

Example

Name of Wood:	Dingle Wood
Type of woodland:	Mixed broadleaf, ancient semi natural
Grid Ref:	ST123123
Size:	8 hectares
Location:	Pixley Marcle, Shropshire
Owner:	Mr and Mrs Cecil Oakes since 2003

1. Woodland assessment

This is an ash/oak woodland of NVC type W10 on a south facing valley slope of a gentle gradient of 1 in 10, that grades into W8 (see Small Woods Directory), of ancient semi natural status on clay over limestone, with an area of sandy loam (Info sheet 3), pH 7.5 to 6.5. The wood has no visible signs of management within the last 10 years, has not been planted and the species growing on the site are those that would naturally occur there. The ash stored coppice was last coppiced some forty years ago. Other tree species include silver birch, with some rowan, with patchy hazel last coppiced some twenty years ago.

There is a rich ground flora with over 100 species of wildflower present (you would attach a full species list) including bluebell, wood anemone, yellow archangel and common dog violet (mentioning indicator species – (see Small Woods Directory-reinforces the fact that it is ancient woodland) with Dog's Mercury a dominant on the clay areas and bramble where it grades into the loamy sand (see Naturalness test in Info Sheet 3).

The wood is not fully stocked with timber, the distance between some ash trees in compartment A and C being 9 metres apart at age 40 (see Info Sheet 3) but there is good ash regeneration at seedling and pole stage (see Small Woods Directory) or there is not a good enough range and number of size classes for a continuous cover individual tree/group felling selection system (see Info Sheet 7).

The size class distribution - again you would attach this - (Info sheets 6 and 7) shows very few mature trees, but there is sufficient natural regeneration to ensure the long term survival of the wood.

Timber volume per hectare is estimated at 150 cubic metres per hectare (from timber sample plots - see info Sheets 6 - attach results) and there are some fine quality ash butts of 40 cms dbh, though some are suppressed and others are forked. The oak is of mixed timber form with much low branching and average dbh of 40 cms. However there are no signs of disease in either the oak or the ash.

Access to the woodland is fairly good being near to the B4545 and the woodland has two main rides that bisect it of limestone construction capable of carrying a forwarder. The vegetation on these rides has closed in to less than 3 metres wide in places, shading out the violets and grass species and there are few butterfly species present including the speckled wood. There are no footpaths in the wood.

Due to the lack of thinning the woodland has predominantly 'thicket' loving species of birds, including treecreeper, wren, garden warbler and long tailed tit, but species such as wood warbler are not present due to the lack of thinning (attach species list).

The wood could be described as 'currently unmanaged'.

2. Objectives of management

1. To manage the woodland to maximise its current and potential value for nature conservation through : increasing the diversity through thinning (including to give more light to the natural regeneration), coppicing 90% of the stored coppice on a 6 then 25 year rotation, recoppicing the hazel on an 8 year rotation and widening bays within the rides for butterfly habitat.

2. To manage the wood to increase its potential for timber and woodland produce as above, to produce as much income as possible on a sustainable basis within the context of managing for nature conservation as an equal objective.

3. To manage the wood with neighbouring owners to control grey squirrels and rabbits and deer and to run a pheasant shoot over 10 days per year.

4. To provide 15 tonnes of green timber a year to be dried to heat a 4 bedroomed house.

3. Opportunities and constraints to achieve the objectives

There is much opportunity to improve the wood for nature conservation through improving the age structure of the wood, especially for birds. Also for butterflies by widening the ride to 10 metres in places running north south. There is also much opportunity to gradually improve the timber value through thinning and recoppicing which will yield at least 20 tonnes of firewood per annum to fully heat the owner's buildings if the owner carries out the thinning work themselves, after training.

There are no significant constraints on this woodland as access is fairly good once the rides are reopened and the site is capable of growing a good crop of timber.

4. Analysis

Having looked at the assessment of what is there, and with no significant constraints, the following has emerged:

i) The wildlife and timber value of the wood can be improved through thinning, removing any suppressed and forked ash and favouring oaks with better form, opening up some of the natural regeneration to light, recoppicing the stored coppice over a 6 then a twenty five year cycle, recoppicing the hazel over an 8 year cycle and installing 20 nest boxes and 5 bat boxes. Also retaining 2 dead standing stems per acre for deadwood habitat in the future.

ii) The wood is capable of being used as a pheasant shoot for the required number of days per year.

iii) The wood is capable of providing the firewood needs of the owner and the oak and ash butts are of sufficient size to be sold as sawlog quality, at roadside felled by the owner for £100 per cubic metre for the oak and £80 per cubic metre for the ash.

5. Management prescriptions and action plan

Compartment No.	Prescription	Timing	Costing	By Whom
A – ash/oak 4ha	Thin on 5 yearly cycle to aim for final crop ash age 65, Oak 120	Begin autumn 1999	Time x no. of days	Owner
B – ash stored coppice 2ha	Recoppice 0.33ha p/a. for firewood Cut 90% of area over 6 years	1999		Contractor

This plan can now form the basis of an application to Forestry Commission for a Woodland Grant Scheme (W.G.S.).

Acknowledgements

I would like to extend my special thanks to:

Derek Patch, Tree Advice Trust, Forestry Commission

Ian Tubby, Forest Services, Forestry Commission

Matt Brocklehurst, Head of Forestry, National Forest Company

Graham Smith, Editor, *Smallholder* magazine

John Greenshields, Blackdown & East Devon Woodland Association

John Leach, woodland owner, Somerset

Jim Rogan, woodland owner, Devon

Will Rolls, Biomass Energy Centre, Forestry Commission

Phillip Poulton, Tree Officer, South Somerset District Council

Victoria Hodson, Communications Manager, The Woodland Trust

Brynley Andrews, Arboricultural Consultant

Andy Higgins, Tree Surgeon, Out On A Limb

Mark Hinsley, Arboricultural Consultant

Photographs

Special thanks to Phil Lockwood of the Woodland Trust and Matt Brocklehurst of The National Forest Company for their help with supplying many inspiring images.

References

A Guide to Creating New Native Woodland, The Woodland Trust

Create a Farm Woodland, Hugh Williams, The National Forest Company

Farm Conservation Guide, AgroEvo UK Ltd, 1995

Farm Woodland Practice, Forestry Commission Handbook, 1988

High Weald Land Manager's Pack, 2011

Natural Communities, O. N. Bishop, John Murray, London, 1973

So You Own a Wood, Forestry Commission, 2009

The Earth Care Manual, Patrick Whitefield, Permanent Publications, 2004

The Wood Fire Handbook, Vincent Thurkettle, Mitchell Beazley, 2012

Tree Detailing, Michael Littlewood, Ecodesignscape, 2013

Trees on the Farm, Farmers Weekly, 1991

Resources

Forestry Commission, 620 Bristol Business Park, Coldharbour Lane, Bristol, BS16 1EJ. Tel: 0117 906 6000. **www.forestry.gov.uk**

The National Forest Company, Bath Lane, Moira, Swadlincote, Derbyshire DE12 6BD. Tel: 01283 551211. **www.nationalforest.org**

Small Woods Association, Station Road, Coalbrookdale, Telford, TF8 7DR. Tel: 01952 432769. **www.smallwoods.org.uk**

Woodland Trust, Kempton Way, Grantham, Lincolnshire NG31 6LL. Tel: 01476 581111. **www.woodlandtrust.org.uk**

National Soil Resource Institute, Cranfield University, College Road, Cranfield, Bedfordshire MK43 0AL. **www.cranfield.ac.uk/sas/nsri/**

Forestry Commission Map Request Form **www.forestry.gov.uk/pdf/MapRequestForm.pdf**

Google Earth http://earth.google.co.uk

Sylva Foundation myForest service (free digital mapping and planning) **www.sylva.org.uk/myforest/**

Arboricultural Association, Ampfield House, Romsey, Hants SO51 9PA. Tel: (01794) 368717. **www.trees.org.uk**

Institute of Chartered Foresters, 59 George Street, Edinburgh EH2 2JG. Tel: (0131) 2401425

Forestry Commission England, Great Eastern House, Tenison Road, Cambridge, CB1 2DU. Tel: (0845) 3673787

Forestry Commission Scotland, 231 Corstophine Road, Edinburgh EH12 7AR. Tel: (0131) 3340303

Forestry Commission Wales/Comisiwn Coedwigaeth Cymru, Victoria Terrace, Aberystwyth, Ceredigion SY23 2DQ. Tel: (0845) 6040845

Forest Stewardship Council, 11-13 Great Oak Street, Llanidloes, Powys SY8 6BU. Tel: 01686 413916. **www.fsc-uk.org.uk**